THE OFFICIAL
ROCKY HORROR PICTURE SHOW™
MOVIE NOVEL™

Edited and Adapted by
Richard J. Anobile

Screenplay by
Jim Sharman & Richard O'Brien

Introduction by
Sal Piro

A & W Visual Library
New York

About the Editor:

RICHARD J. ANOBILE is one of the foremost producers of film-related books in the United States. He has edited several in a film comedy series, including the best-selling *Why a Duck?*

Anobile pioneered the use of the frame blow-up technique to re-create entire films in book form and the result, *The Film Classics Library,* has been widely hailed in the U.S. and Europe.

Other Anobile books include the international bestseller *The Marx Bros. Scrapbook* (Groucho Marx, co-author), *The Making of Rich Man, Poor Man, Beyond Open Marriage* (Ulla Anobile, co-author), *The Mork and Mindy Video Novel, The Battlestar Galactica Photo Story,* and the *Alien Movie Novel.*

Anobile studied at the City University of New York's Institute of Film Technique. He now resides in Hollywood where, in addition to continuing his work in publishing, he is also developing various television and feature film projects. His next book will be *Star Trek — The Photo Story.*

Frame blow-ups by Ryan Herz and Mark Henry.

Designed by Harry Chester, Inc.

Introduction

THE ROCKY HORROR PICTURE SHOW™

... midnights Friday and Saturday sell-out crowds ... audiences go wild ... madness takes its toll.

To the unenlightened (virgins to us) arises the question: What is all the fuss about *The Rocky Horror Picture Show?* From the thousands of fans across the country come varied replies and responses. The answers are varied because the fans themselves have created this "fuss." And the reason for *everyone's* response to *Rocky Horror* is particularly personal to them.

For the first time in cinematic history, the audiences have attached themselves to a film so strongly that they have actually taken over. These audience participants talk back to the screen, makeup and dress as the characters, utilize props and parallel the film's action.

This phenomenon goes beyond the physical routines of the participants. What makes it so infectious is the feeling of family and community within the theaters, the sense of creativity and expression that is brought forth and the outright fun and excitement of it all. Most importantly, a feeling of love pervades this cult as they give themselves over to pleasure and exhort the philosophy of becoming all the things they have dreamed. This response will invade the '80s and continue in the outlook of all *Rocky's* followers throughout their lives.

This Movie Novel™ is a frame-by-frame memory of this movie that will always be special to all of us. Read. Cherish. Enjoy.

SAL PIRO
President of The National *Rocky Horror Picture Show* Fan Club

Michael Rennie was ill
The day the earth stood still
But he told us where we stand
And Flash Gordon was there
In silver underwear
Claude Rains was the invisible man.
Then something went wrong
For Fay Wray and King Kong
They got caught in a celluloid jam
Then at a deadly pace
It came from outer space
And this is how the message ran:

Science fiction — double feature
Dr. X will build a creature
See androids fighting Brad and Janet
Anne Francis stars in Forbidden Planet
Ah-ha ha-ho
At the late-night double-feature picture show

I knew Leo G. Carroll
Was over a barrel
When tarantula took to the hills
And I really got hot
When I saw Jeanette Scott
Fight a Triffid that spits poison and kills
Dana Andrews said prunes
Gave him the runes
And passing them used lots of skills
And when worlds collide
Said George Pal to his bride
I'm gonna give you some terrible thrills
Like a —

Science fiction — double feature
Dr. X will build a creature
See androids fighting Brad and Janet
Anne Francis stars in Forbidden Planet
Oh-ho
At the late-night double-feature picture show

(I wanna go – o – o)
To the late-night double-feature picture show
(By RKO)
Oh – o – o
To the late-night double-feature picture show
(In the back row)
Oh – o – o
To the late-night double-feature picture show

"Here they come!"

"Yes, all the
close family."

CLICK!

"Hey, Ralph!" says Brad.
"Well, Brad, I guess we really did it, huh?" says Ralph.
"I don't think there's any doubt about that, Ralph."

"You and Betty have almost been inseparable since you sat in on Dr. Scott's refresher course," continues Brad.

"Well, to tell you the truth, Brad, that was the only reason I showed up in the first place!"

"Okay, you guys," shouts Betty. "This is it! Are you ready?"

"Hey, Brad, Betty's going to throw her bouquet!"

"Hey, big fella, looks like it could be your turn next," chides Ralph.

Who knows?

I've got it! I've got it!

"So long, see you, Brad,"
exclaims Ralph.
"See you, Ralph."

"Oh, Brad, wasn't it wonderful!"
Janet blurts out.
"Didn't Betty look radiantly beautiful?"

I can't believe
that an hour ago she
was plain old Betty Monroe.
And now, now she's
Mrs. Ralph Hapschatt.

"Ralph's a lucky guy," answers Brad.

"Yes," Janet agrees.

"Er, everyone knows Betty's a wonderful little cook," continues Brad. "Gosh, Ralph'll be lined up for a promotion in a year or two!"

"Hey, Janet!"

"Yes, Brad?"

"I've got something to say. I really loved the, ah, um ... skillful way you beat the other girls to the bride's bouquet!"

Oh ... oh Brad!

"The river was deep,
But I swam it."

"The future is ours,
So let's plan it."

Janet

Janet

"So please don't tell me
to can it."

Janet

"I have one thing to say
And that's 'Dammit, Janet!'"

"The road was long,
But I ran it."

Janet

"There's a fire
in my heart,
And you fan it."

Janet

"If there's one
fool for you,
Then I am it."

Janet

"I've got one
thing to say
And that's "

"Here's a ring to
prove that
I'm no joker."

"There's three ways
that love can grow."
"That's good, bad or mediocre."

"Oh!"

"Oh J—A—N—E—T
I love you so!"

"Oh, it's nicer than
Betty Monroe had.
Oh Brad."

"Now we're engaged and
I'm so glad."
"Oh Brad."
"That you met Mom
And you know Dad."
"Oh Brad."

"I've one thing to say
and that's
'Brad, I'm mad for
you too!' "

"There's one thing left to do
—ah—ooh!"

"And that's go see the man who began it."
"Janet."

"When we met in his science exam, It made me give you the eye and then panic."

"I've got one thing to say and that's 'Dammit, Janet, I love you!'"

I would like, if I may, to take you on a strange journey.

It seemed a fairly ordinary night when Brad Majors and his fiancée, Janet Weiss, two young ordinary healthy kids, left Denton that late November evening to visit a Dr. Everett Scott, ex-tutor and now a friend of both of them.

It's true there were dark storm clouds, heavy, black and pendulous, toward which they were driving. It is also true that the spare tire they were carrying was badly in need of some air.

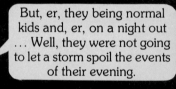

But, er, they being normal kids and, er, on a night out ... Well, they were not going to let a storm spoil the events of their evening.

"Gosh! That's the third motorcyclist that's passed us. They certainly take their lives into their hands what with the weather and all!"

"Yes, Janet, life's pretty cheap to that type."

"What's the matter, Brad, darling?"

"Hmm. We must have taken the wrong fork a few miles back."
"But," questions Janet, "where did the motorcyclists come from?"
"Hmm. Well, I guess we will have to turn back."

"What was that bang!"

"We must have a blowout! Dammit! I knew I should have gotten that spare tire fixed! Well, you just stay here and keep warm and I'll go for help."

"Where will you go?" asks Janet. "We're in the middle of nowhere!"

Brad wonders, "Didn't we pass a castle back down the road a few miles? Maybe they have a telephone I could use."

"I'm going with you," says Janet.

"Oh, no darling," pleads Brad. "There's no sense in both of us getting wet!"

Janet is firm. "I'm coming with you!" Then she adds coyly, "Besides, darling, that owner of the phone might be a beautiful woman and you might never come back again."
Brad laughs.

LATER:

ENTER AT YOUR OWN RISK!!

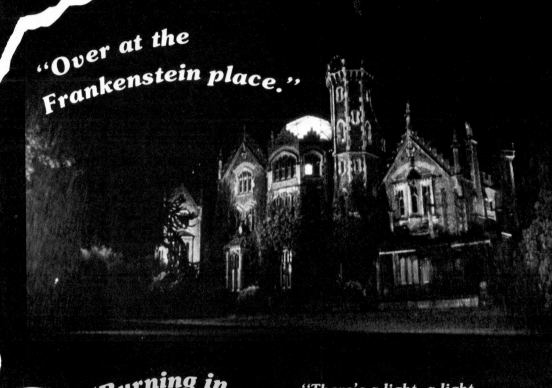

"Over at the Frankenstein place."

"Burning in the fireplace."

There's a light!

"There's a light, a light in the darkness of everybody's life."

VROOOM!

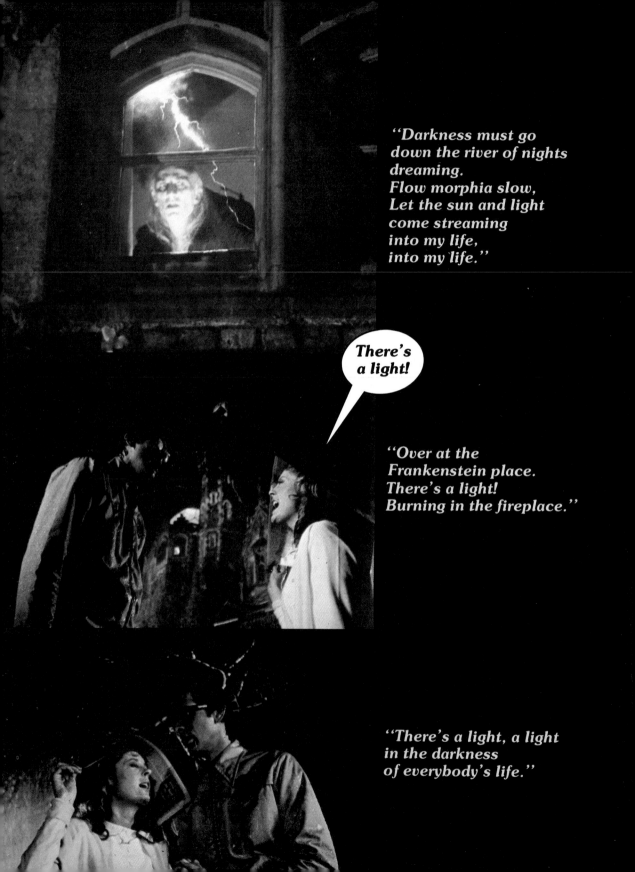

And so it seemed that fortune had smiled on Brad and Janet and that they had found the assistance that their plight required. Or had they?

"Oh, Brad, let's go back. I'm cold and frightened."
"Just a moment, Janet. They may have a telephone."

"Hello."

"Hi! My name is Brad Majors, and this is my fiancée, Janet Weiss! I wonder if you might help us. You see, our car broke down a few miles up the road. Do you have a phone we might use?"

"You're wet."

"Yes," says Janet. "It's raining."
"Yes," agrees Brad.
"Yes," echoes Riff Raff.

"I think you'd better both come inside."

"You're too kind!"

"Oh, Brad!
I'm frightened.
What kind of
place is this?"

"Oh, it's
probably
some kind of
hunting lodge
for rich weirdos,"
suggests Brad.

"This way,"
commands
Riff Raff.

"Are you having a party?"
Janet asks.

Riff Raff answers tersely,
"You've arrived on a rather
special night. It's one of
the master's affairs."

"Oh, lucky him!"
Janet meekly exclaims.

Magenta's shriek startles the couple. "You're lucky! He's lucky! I'm lucky! We're all lucky! Ha. Ha. Ha!"

"It's astounding. Time is fleeting."

"Madness takes its toll."

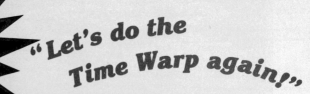

"Let's do the Time Warp again!"

"Let's do the Time Warp again!"

"*But it's the pelvic thrust,*
That really drives you insane."

Let's
do the
Time Warp
again!

**"Let's do
the Time
Warp again!"**

"Let's do the Time Warp again!"

It's a jump to the left.

"And then a step to the right."

"Let's do the
Time Warp again!"

THUMP!

"Let's do the Time Warp again!"

It's just a jump to the left!

"And then a step to the right."

With your hands on your hips!

"You bring your knees in tight.

But it's the pelvic thrust, That really drives you insane."

"Let's do the Time Warp again!"

"Let's do the Time Warp again!"

"Brad, say something!"

"Say!" yells Brad.

"Do any of you guys know how to Madison?"

"Brad, please, let's get out of here."

"Janet, for God's sake, keep a grip on yourself!"

"But, Brad, it seems so unhealthy here!"

"It's just a party, Janet."

"Well, I want to go!"

"Janet, we can't go anywhere until I get to a phone."

"Well, then ask the butler or someone!"

"Just a moment, Janet. We don't want to interfere with their celebration."

"Brad, this isn't the Junior Chamber of Commerce!"

"Look, Janet, they're probably foreigners with ways different from our own. They may do some more folk dancing!"

"Look, I'm cold, I'm wet, and I'm just plain scared!"

"I'm here. There's nothing to worry about!" Brad assures Janet.

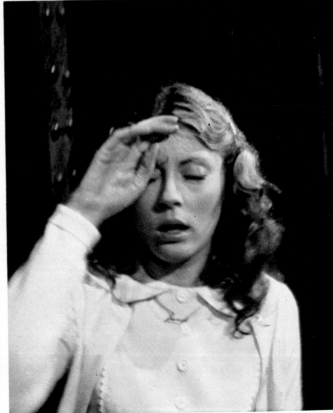

*"How do you do?
I see you've met my
faithful handyman.
He's a little brought down,
Because when you knocked,
He thought you were the
candyman."*

*"Don't get strung out
by the way that I look.
Don't judge a book
by its cover."*

*"I'm not much of a man
by the light of day,
But by night I'm one
hell of a . . ."*

"Lover!"

*"I'm just
a sweet
Transvestite
from Transexual
Transylvania."*

*"Let me show you around,
Maybe play you a sound."*

*"You both look
like you're
pretty groovie!"*

*"Or if you want
something visual,
But not abysmal,
We could take in an old
Steve Reeves movie!"*

"Well you got caught
with a flat,
Well how about that!
Well babes
don't you panic."

"By the light of
the night,
It'll all seem all right.
I'll get you a
satanic mechanic!"

"I could show you my favorite obsession. I've been making a man with blonde hair and a tan. And he's good for relieving my Tension!"

"I'm just a sweet Transvestite."

"I'm just a sweet Transvestite from Transexual..."

"Transylvania!"

"So come up to the lab."

"And see what's on the slab."

"I see you shiver with antici-pation!"

"But maybe the rain
is really the blame.
So I'll remove the cause . . ."

"But not the symptom!"

"Oh! Thank you."

"Thank you, er, very much."

"Oh! Oh! Brad!"

"It's all right, Janet. We'll play along for now and pull out the aces when the time is right."

Eyeing Brad and Janet, Columbia pleads, "Oh slowly, slowly! It's too nice a job to rush."

"Hi! My name is Brad Majors and this is my fiancee Janet Weiss! Er, and you are?"

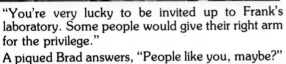

"You're very lucky to be invited up to Frank's laboratory. Some people would give their right arm for the privilege."

A piqued Brad answers, "People like you, maybe?"

"Huh! I've seen it!"

"Come along. The Master doesn't like to be kept waiting."

Trying to be friendly under the circumstances, Janet asks Magenta, "Is he, um, Frank, I mean ... is he your husband?"

Riff Raff answers, "The Master is not yet married. Nor do I think he ever will be. We are simply his servants."

"Oh," replies Janet.

"Magenta! Columbia! Go and assist Riff Raff."

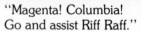

I will entertain ... em ... em ...

"Brad Majors!"

"This is my fiancée, Janet Vice, er Weiss."

"Well, how nice! And what charming underclothes you both have!"

Enchanté!

"But here, put these on. They'll make you feel less, er, vulnerable."

"It's not often we receive visitors here, let alone offer them hospitality."

"Hospitality! All we wanted to do was use your telephone, Goddammit! A reasonable request which you have chosen to ignore!"

"Brad," implores Janet. "Don't be ungrateful!"
"Ungrateful!" fumes Brad.

"How forceful you are, Brad!"

"Such a perfect specimen of manhood, so dominant!"

"You must be awfully proud of him, Janet."

"Well," whimpers Janet, "Yes, I am."

"Do you have any tattoos, Brad?"

"Certainly not!"

"How about you?" Frank jokingly asks Janet.

Riff Raff interrupts. "Everything is in readiness, Master. We merely await your word."

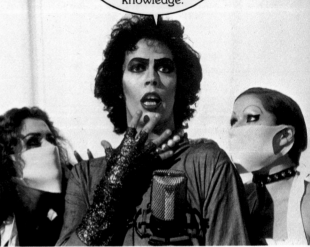

You see, you are fortunate ... For tonight is the night that my beautiful creature is destined to be born!

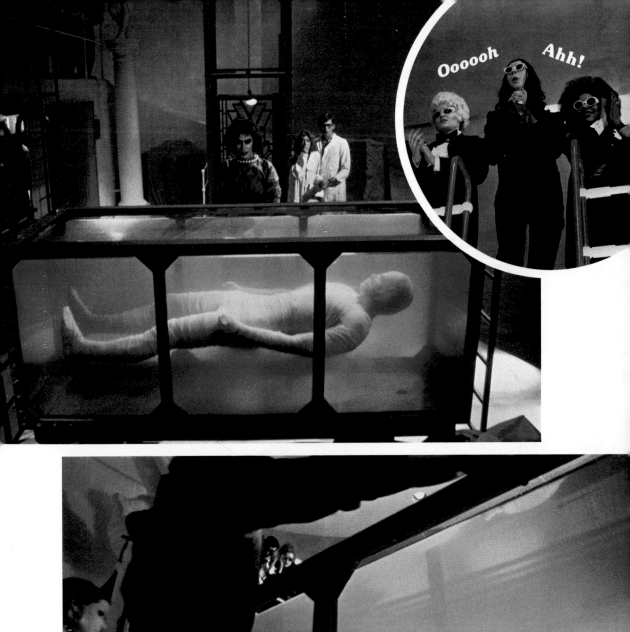

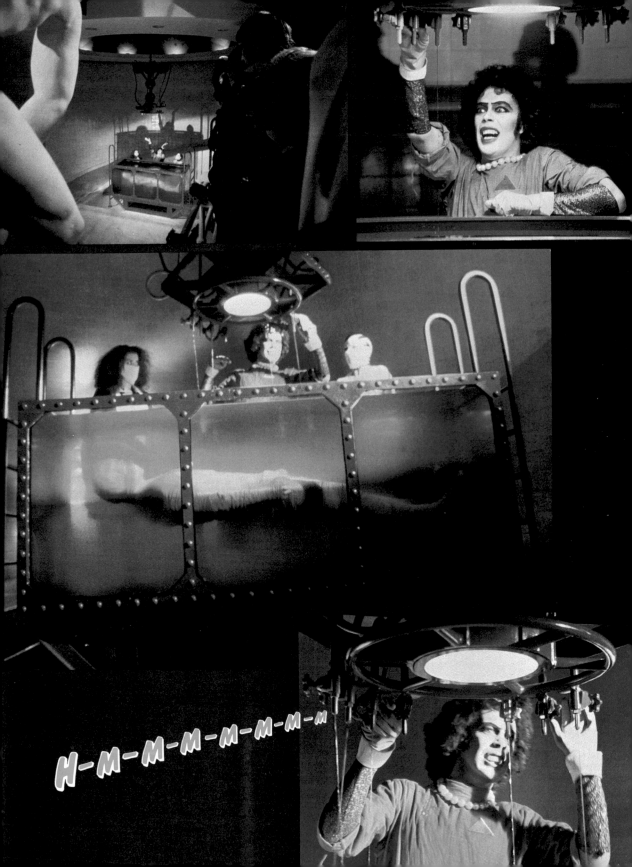

H-M-M-M-M-M-M-M

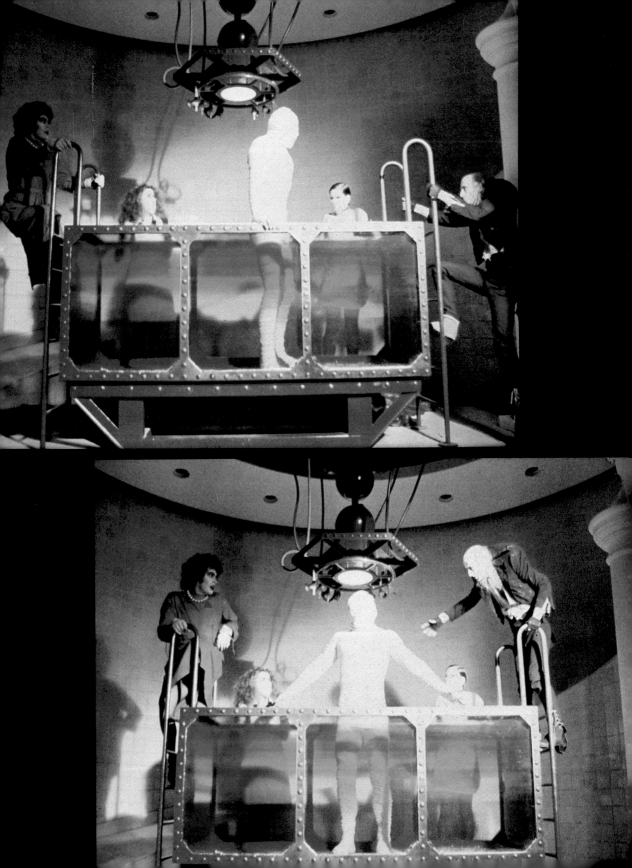

"The sword of Damocles is hanging over my head.

And I've got a feeling someone's going to be cutting the thread."

"Oh, the woe is me,
My life is a misery."

"Oh, can't you see that
I'm at the start
of a pretty big downer."

"I woke up this morning
with a start
when I fell out of bed."

"The sword of Damocles is
hanging over my head.
And I've got the feeling someone's
going to be cutting the thread."

"Oh, woe is me.
My life is a mystery.
Oh, can't you see that
I'm at the start
of a pretty big downer."

"Well, really! That's no way to behave on your first day out! Oh, well, er, but since you're such an exceptional beauty, I'm prepared to forgive you."

"Oh, I just love success!"

"Okay? Just okay! I think we can do better than that!"

"Well, Brad and Janet,
what do you think of him?"

"Well, I don't like men
with too many muscles."

"I didn't make him for you!"

He carries
the Charles Atlas
seal of approval!

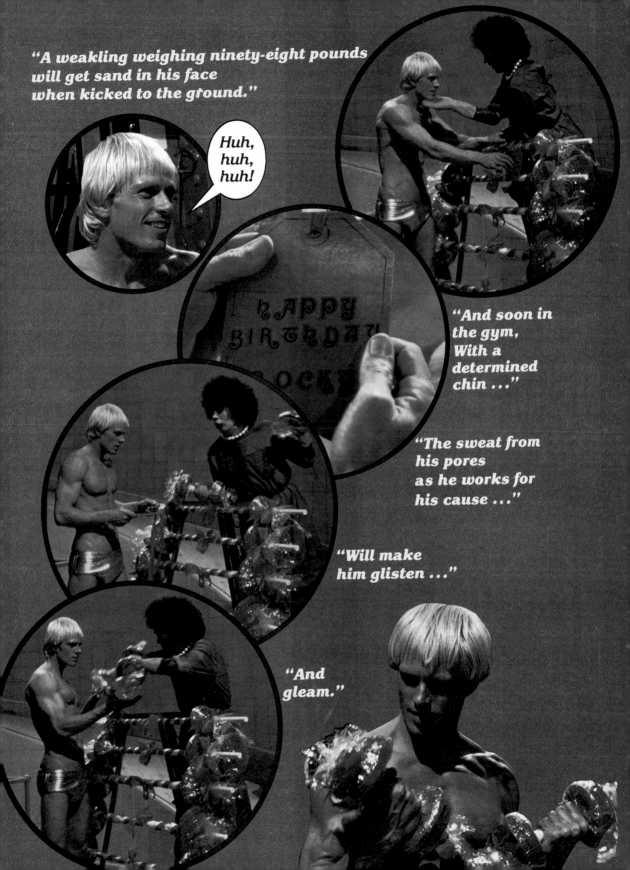

"And with massage,
And just a little bit of..."   "Stea—e—eam!"

"Hm, ha-ha, ha-har!"   "He'll be pink and quite clean."

"He'll be a
strong man..."   "Oh, honey!
But the wrong man."

"He'll eat nutritious high protein,
And swallow raw eggs."

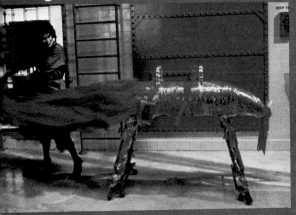

"Try to build up his shoulders ..."

"His chest, arms ..."

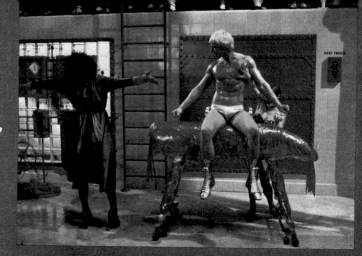

"In just seven days,
I can make you a
ma—aa—a—a—an!"

"He'll do press-ups
and chin-ups.
Do the snatch,
Clean and jerk."

"He thinks dynamic tension
must be hard work.
Such strenuous living
I just don't understand."

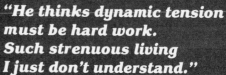

"When in just seven days—
Oh baby!"

I can make you a
ma—a—a—a—an!

Come on now!

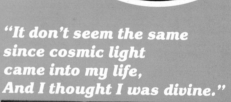

*"Whatever happened to
Saturday night,
When you dressed up sharp,
And you felt all right!"*

*"It don't seem the same
since cosmic light
came into my life,
And I thought I was divine."*

"I used to go for a ride with a chick who'd go and listen to the radio."

"Hot patootie! Bless my soul!"

"A saxophone was blowing on a rock-and-roll show."

"I really love that rock and roll!"

"And we climbed in the back seat and we really had a good time."

"Hot patootie!
Bless my soul!
I really love that rock and roll!"

"Hot patootie!
Bless my soul!
I really love
that rock
and roll!"

Lovely party.

"My head it used to swim
from the perfume I smelled.
My hands kind of fumbled
with her white plastic belt.
I'd taste her baby-pink lipstick
and that's when I'd melt."

"And she whispered in my ear tonight she was really mine, Get back in front and put some hair oil on."

"It felt pretty good—whooooo! Really had a good ti—i—ime!"

"Buddy Holly was singing his very last song."

"Hot patootie! Bless my soul! I really love that rock and roll!"

"Hot patootie! Bless my soul! I really love that rock and roll!"

"With your arms around your girl you tried to, ah, sing along."

*"Hot patootie!
Bless my soul!
I really love that
rock and roll!"*

*"Hot patootie!
Bless my soul!
I really
love that
rock and roll!"*

NOOOO!

NOOOO!

"One for the vaults!"

"Oooooh"

"But a deltoid and a bicep!"

"A hot groin and a tricep,
Makes me ooooh!--Shake."

"Makes we want to take
Charles Atlas by the ha..aa..and!"

"In just seven days, oh, baby!
I can make you a Ma–ha–ha–haan!"

I'm a muscle fan!

"I don't want no dissension."

"In just seven days,
I can make you a
Ma–ha–ha–haan!"
"Dig it if you can!
In just seven days,
I can make you a
Ma–ha–ha–haan!"

"Just dynamic tension!"

"Rocky and Frank!
Rah! Rah! Rah!
Rocky and Frank!
Rah! Rah! Rah!"

There are those who say that life is an illusion, that reality is simply a figment of the imagination!

If this is so, then Brad and Janet are quite safe.

However, the sudden departure of their host into the seclusion of his somber bridal suite had left them feeling both apprehensive and uneasy.

A feeling which grew as the guests departed and they were shown to their separate rooms.

Oh!

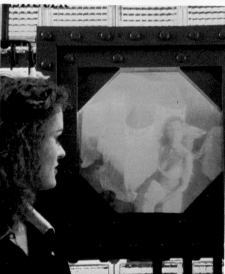

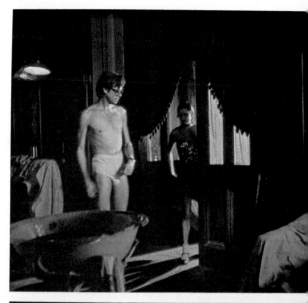

LATER: *KNOCK!* *KNOCK!*

Oh! Oh! It's you!

Who is it? Who's there?

It's only me, Janet.

I'm afraid so, Janet. But isn't it nice!

Oh, Brad! Come in.

Oh, you beast, you monster! What have you done with Brad?

Er, well nothing. Why, do you think I should?

Oh Brad —mmmmm— oh yes, my darling! But, what if . . .

It's all right, Janet. Everything's going to be all right.

Oh, I hope so darling.

You tricked me! I wouldn't have! I've never, never!

Yes, yes I know, but it isn't all bad is it?

MEANWHILE:

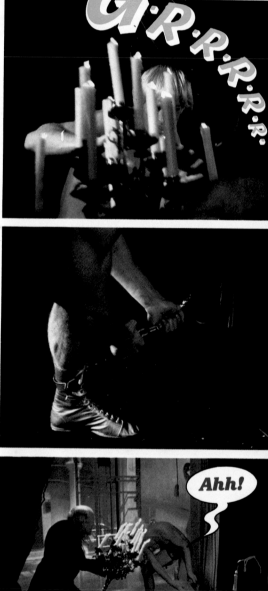

G·R·R·R·R

AT THAT VERY MOMENT:

"Brad?"

"What's
happening
here?"

"Where's
anybody!"

"Brad, my darling. How could
I have done this to you?"

"Oh! If only we
hadn't made
this journey!"

"If only the
car hadn't
broken down!"

"If only we were amongst
friends— or sane persons!"

"Oh, Brad! What have they done with him!"   "Oh! Brad! How could you?"

"You're hurt! Did *they* do this to you?"

"Here, I'll dress your wounds.
Poor baby! There."

Emotion: agitation or disturbance of mind; vehement or excited mental state.

It is also a powerful and irrational master. And from what Magenta and Columbia eagerly viewed on their television monitor, there seemed little doubt that Janet was indeed it's slave.

Tell us about it, Janet!

"I was feeling done in, couldn't win. I'd only ever kissed before."

"I thought there's no use getting into heavy petting. It only leads to trouble and seat wetting."

*"Touch–a, touch–a, touch–a touch me!
I wanna be dirty!"*

*"Thrill me.
Chill me.
Fulfill me!"*

"Creature of the night!"

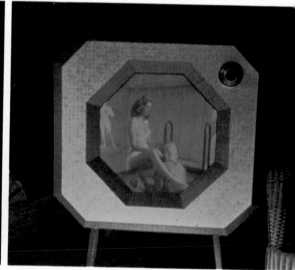

SEVERAL MOMENTS LATER:

"Master!"   "Oh!"

"Well, see if you can find him
on the monitor!" commands Frank.

"How did it happen? I understood you
to be watching!"

"I was only away for a minute, Master."

"Master! Master!
We have a visitor."

"Scotty! Dr. Everett Scott!" yelps Brad. "You know this earthling, er, person?" stutters Riff Raff. "I most certainly do!" says Brad. "He happens to be an old friend of mine!"

"I see! So this wasn't simply a chance meeting. You came here with a purpose."

"I told you, my car broke down. I'm telling the truth!" "I know what you told me, Brad. But this Dr. Everett Scott, his name is not unknown to me!"

"He was a science teacher at Denton High School!" says Brad. But Frank persists. "And now he works for your government, doesn't he, Brad? He's attached to the bureau of investigation of what you call U.F.O.'s!"

"He might be! I don't know!"

"The intruder is entering the building, Master."

"Shall we enquire of
him in person?"

H-M-M-M-M-M-M

I hope you're adaptable, Dr. Scott! I know Brad is!

I can assure you that Brad's presence here comes as a complete surprise to me. I came here to find Eddie.

"Eddie!" says Brad. "I've seen him! He's …"

Frank cuts Brad short. "Eddie? What do you know of Eddie, Dr. Scott?"

I happen to know a great deal about a lot! You see, Eddie happens to be my nephew!

Oh!

"Master, dinner is prepared!"

"Excellent! Under the circumstances formal dress is to be optional."

Food has always played a vital role in life's rituals. The breaking of the bread, the last meal of the condemned man, and now *this* meal. However informal it might appear, you can be sure there was to be very little *bonhomie*.

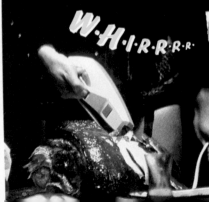

W·H·I·R·R·r·r

"A toast. To absent friends."

"To absent friends."

"And Rocky!"

"Happy birthday to you."

"Happy birthday to you."

"Happy birthday dear Rocky!
Happy birthday to you."

"Shall we?"

"We came here to discuss Eddie." "Eddie!"

"It's a rather tender subject. Another slice, anyone?"
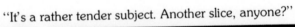

"I knew he was in with a bad crowd.
But it was worse than I imagined. Aliens!"

"Aliens!"

"Go on, Dr. Scott.
Or should I say
Dr. von Scott?"

"What exactly are you implying?"

"That's all right,
Brad."

*"From the day he was born
he was trouble.
He was the thorn in his mother's side.
She tried in vain ..."*

*"But he never caused her
nothing but shame."*

*"He left home the
day she died.*

*From the day
she was gone,
All he wanted ..."*

"Was rock-and-roll porn."

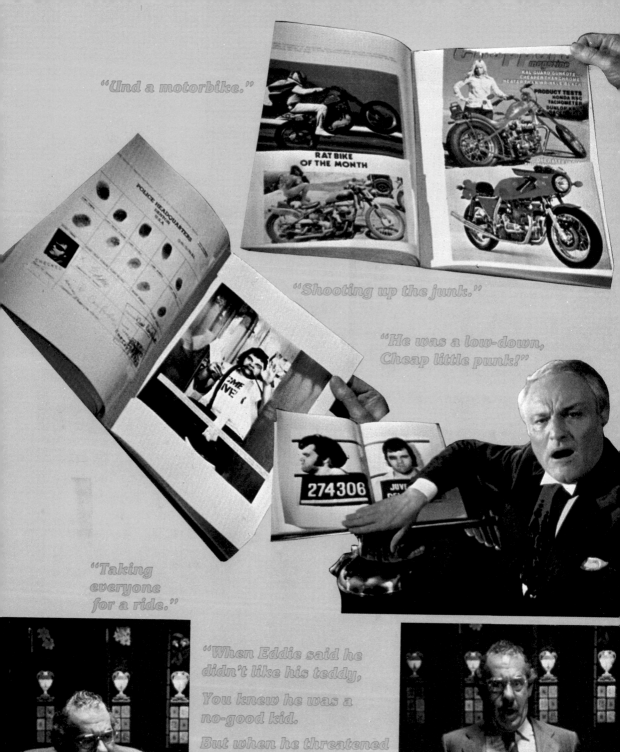

"Und a motorbike."

RAT BIKE OF THE MONTH

"Shooting up the junk."

"He was a low-down, Cheap little punk!"

274306

"Taking everyone for a ride."

"When Eddie said he didn't like his teddy,

You knew he was a no-good kid.

But when he threatened your life,

With a switchblade knife ..."

"What a guy?"

"Und I did."

"Makes you cry?"

"Everybody shoved him, I very nearly loved him."

"I said, 'Hey listen to me, Stay sane inside insanity,' But he locked the door, And threw away the key."

"But he must have been drawn into something,
Making him warn me in a note which reads . . ."

"What's
it say?
What's
it say!"

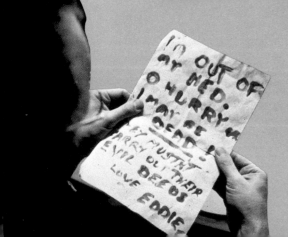

"When Eddie said he didn't like his teddy, You knew he was a no-good kid!"

"But when he threatened your life, With a switchblade knife ..."

What a guy

Makes you cry.

Woe! Woe! Woe!

Hey! Hey! Hey!

Und I did.

"Oh, Rocky! How could you!"

"This way, this way!"

*"I'll tell you once,
I won't tell you twice.
You'd better wise up,
Janet Weiss."*

*"Your apple pie,
Don't taste too nice.
You'd better wise up,
Janet Weiss."*

Oh!

**MEAN-
WHILE:**

*"I've laid the seed,
It should be all you need."*

*"You're as sensual
as a pencil.
Wound up like an 'E'
or first string.
When we made it
did ya hear a bell ring?"*

"Y'got a block.
Well, take my advice.
You'd better wise up,
Janet Weiss!"

"The transducer
will seduce yah!"

"It's something you'll get used to. A mental mind-fuck can be nice!"

You mean he's gonna send us to another planet!

"Planet! Schmanet! Janet!!"

"You'd better wise up, Janet Weiss.
You'd better wise up, build your thighs up."

"You'd better wise up ..."

And then she cried out.

Sto-o-o-op!

"Don't get hot and flustered, Use a bit of mustard!"

"You're a hot dog, but you better not try to hurt her, Frankfurter!"

"My God, I can't stand any more of this! First you spurn me for Eddie, then you slash him up like an old overcoat for Rocky!"

"You chew people up, then you spit them out again! I loved you! Yeah, I loved you and what did it get me. Yeah, I'll tell you. A big nothing!"

"You're like a sponge. You take, take, take and drain everyone of their love and emotion. Yeah, I've had enough. You've got to choose between me and Rocky, so named because of the rocks in his head!"

ZAP!

It's not easy having a good time!

"Even smiling makes my face ache!"

ZAP!

"And my children turn on me! Rocky's behaving just the way that Eddie did. Do you think I made a mistake splitting his brain between the two of them?"

"I grow weary of this world! When shall we return to Transylvania, huh?"

"Come! We are ready for the floor show."

"Magenta, I am indeed grateful to both you and your brother, Riff Raff. You have both served me well. Loyalty such as yours shall not go unrewarded. You will discover that when the mood takes me I can be quite generous."

Magenta snarls, "I ask for nothing, Master!"
As Frank storms off, he screams in anger, "And you shall receive it in abundance!"

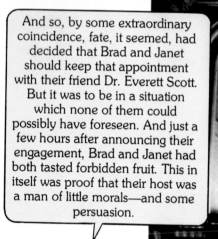

And so, by some extraordinary coincidence, fate, it seemed, had decided that Brad and Janet should keep that appointment with their friend Dr. Everett Scott. But it was to be in a situation which none of them could possibly have foreseen. And just a few hours after announcing their engagement, Brad and Janet had both tasted forbidden fruit. This in itself was proof that their host was a man of little morals—and some persuasion.

What further indignities were they to be subjected to? And what of the floor show that had been spoken of? In an empty house, in the middle of the night, what diabolical plan had seized Frank's crazed imagination? What indeed? From what had gone on before it was clear that this was to be no picnic.

DE·MEDUS

ZAP!

"It was great when it all began,
I was a regular Frankie fan."

"But it was over when he had the plan,
To start working on a muscle man."

"Now the only thing that
gives me hope,
Is my love of a certain dope.
Rose tints my world,
Keeps me safe from my
trouble and pain."

"I'm just seven hours old,
Truly beautiful to behold."

ZAP!

ZAP!

"And somebody should be told,
My libido hasn't been controlled."

"Now the only thing I've come to trust,
Is an orgasmic rush of lust.
Rose tints my world,
Keeps me safe from my trouble and pain."

"It's beyond me!
Help me Mommy!"

"I'll be good
you'll see,
Take this dream
away from me."

"What's this, let's see,
I feel sexy.
What's come over me."

"Woa!
Here it
comes again!"

ZAP!

"Oh, I feel released,
Bad times deceased.
My confidence has increased,
Reality is here."

"The game has
been disbanded,
My mind has
been expanded.
It's a gas that
Frankie has landed."

"His lust is
so sincere!"

KISS!

"Whatever happened
to Fay Wray,
That delicate
satin-draped frame.
As it clung to
her thigh,
How I started
to cry ..."

" 'Cause I wanted
to be dressed
just the same!"

"Give yourself over to absolute pleasure, Swim the warm waters of sins of the flesh."

"Erotic nightmares beyond any measure. And sensual daydreams to treasure forever."

"Can't you just see it! Oh, oh, ohhhh!"

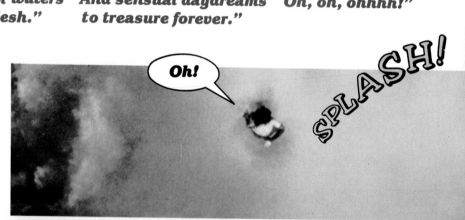

"Don't dream it, Be it. Don't dream it, Be it."

*"Don't dream it,
Be it."*

*"Don't dream it,
Be it."*

*"Don't
dream it,
Be it.
Don't
dream it,
Be it."*

*"Don't
dream it,
Be it."*

"Don't
dream it,
Be it."

"Ach! We've got to get out of this trap
before this decadence saps our wills!"

"I've got to be strong and try
to hang on.
Or else my mind may well SNAP!"

"Und my life will be lived for the . . ."

"THRI–I–I–IL!!!!!"

"It's beyond me,
Help me Mommy!"

"God bless
Lilly St. Cyr!"

"My, my, my!
My, my, my!"

"I'm a wild and an
untamed thing!
I'm a bee with a
deadly sting!
You gotta hit,
And your mind
goes ping!
Your heart'll thump,
And your blood
will sing!"

"So let the party and
the sounds rock on,
We're gonna shake it
till the life has gone.
Rose tint my world,
Keep me safe from my
trouble and pain!"

"We're wild and untamed things!
We're bees with a deadly sting!
You gotta hit, and your mind goes ping!
Your heart'll thump, and your blood will sing!"

"So let the party and the sounds rock on,
We're gonna shake it till the life is gone!
Rose tint my world,
Keep me safe from my trouble and pain!"

"Frank N. Furter,
It's all over."

"Your mission is a failure,
Your lifestyle's too extreme!"

"I'm your new commander.
You are now my prisoner.
We return to Transylvania."

"Prepare the transit beam!"

"Wait! I can explain!"

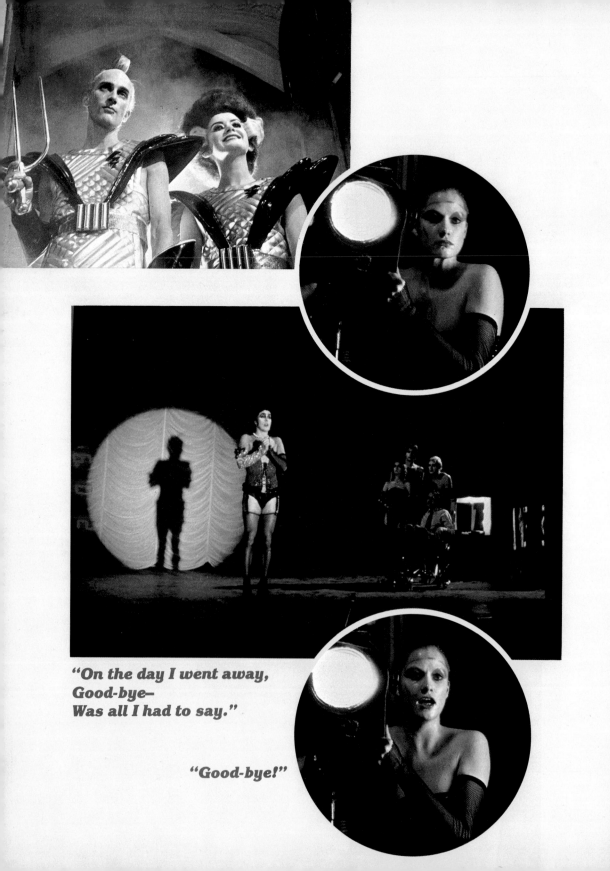

*"On the day I went away,
Good-bye–
Was all I had to say."*

"Good-bye!"

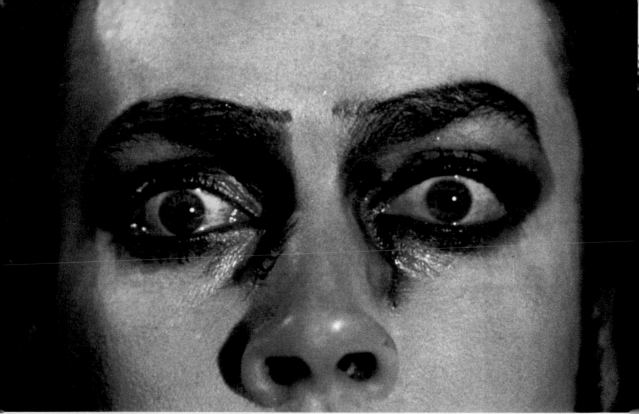

"I'm going home."

"Everywhere it's
been the same,
Feeling ..."

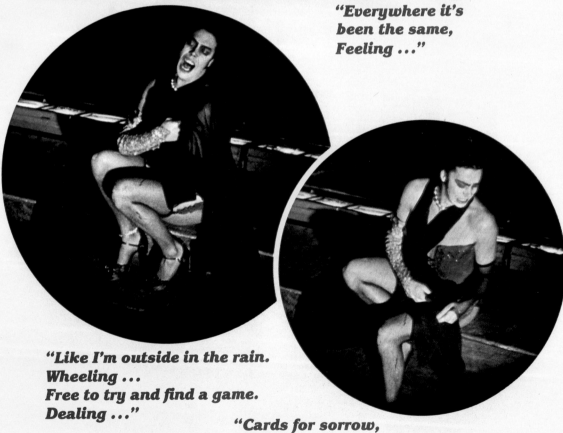

"Like I'm outside in the rain.
Wheeling ...
Free to try and find a game.
Dealing ..."

"Cards for sorrow,
Cards for pain."

" 'Cause I've seen blue skies,
Through the tears in my eyes."

"I'm going home."

"I'm going home."

"I'm going home."

"I'm going home!"

"How sentimental!" sneers Magenta.

"And also
presumptuous
of you," adds
Riff Raff.

"You see, when
I said 'we' were
to return to
Transylvania,
I referred only
to Magenta and
myself.
I'm sorry,
however, if
you found my
words
misleading."

"But you see,
you are to
remain here—
in spirit
anyway."

"Great heavens!"
gulps Dr. Scott.
"That's a laser!"

"Yes, Dr. Scott,
a laser capable
of emitting a
beam of pure
anti-matter."

"You mean you're
going to kill
him?" Brad
questions.
"What's his crime?"

Dr. Scott answers,
"You saw what
became of Eddie!
Society must be
protected."

"Exactly, Dr. Scott.
And now Frank N. Furter,
your time has come."

"Say good-bye to all
of this—and hello
to oblivion!"

EEEEEE!

BLAST!

RRIIPP!

OoOohh!!

BLAST!

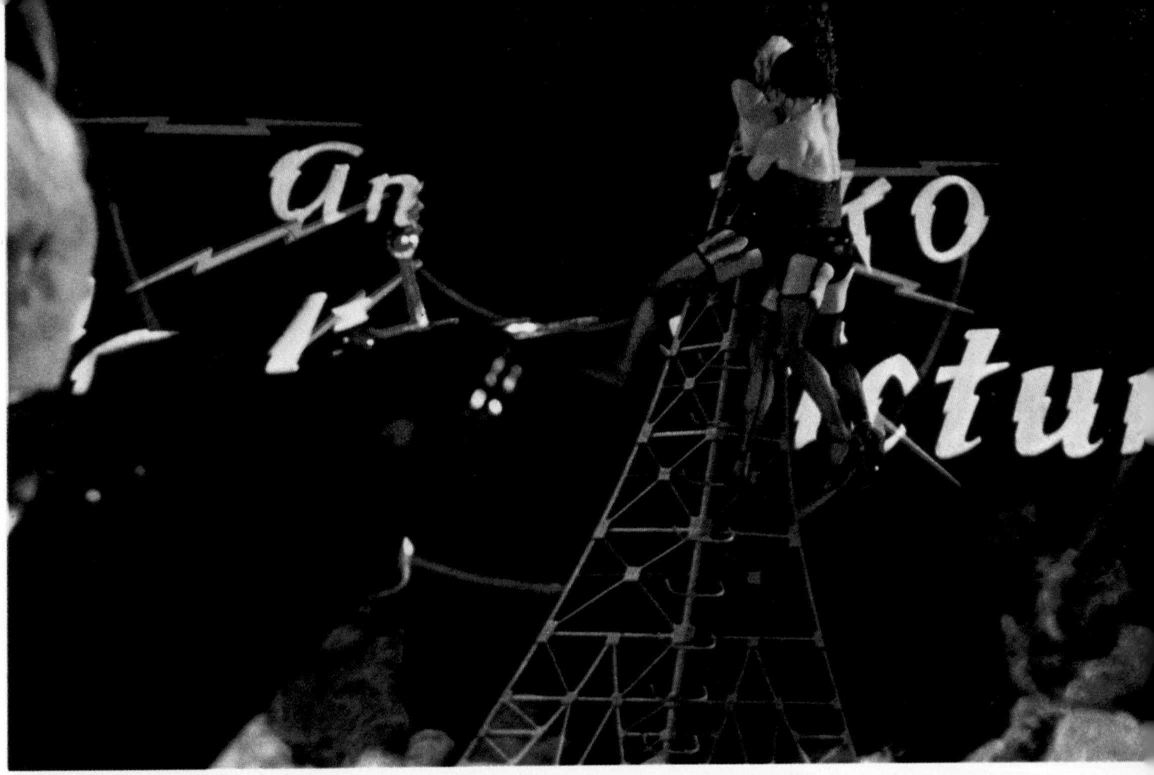
An

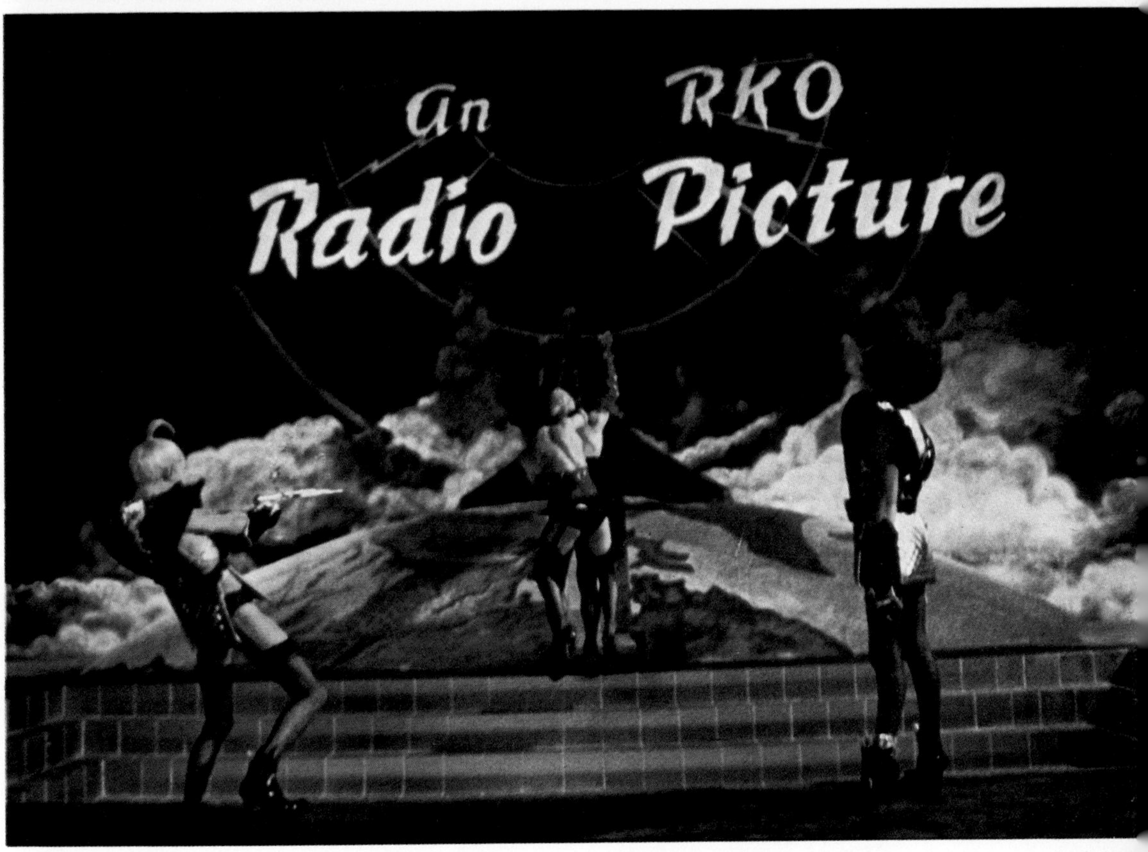
An RKO
Radio Picture

"You've killed them," murmurs Janet.

"But I thought you liked them?" adds Magenta. "They liked you!"

Riff Raff screams, "They didn't like me! They never liked me!"

"You did right!" interrupts Dr. Scott.

"A decision had to be made," Riff Raff says cooly.

Dr. Scott quickly adds, "You're okay by me!"

"Dr. Scott," says Riff Raff, "I'm sorry about your nephew."

"Eddie!" remarks Scott. "Well, perhaps it was for the best."

"You should leave now, Dr. Scott, while it is still possible. We are about to beam the entire house back to the planet of Transexual in the galaxy of Transylvania."

"Go—now!"

"Our noble mission is almost completed, my most beautiful sister. Soon we shall return to the moon-drenched shores of our beloved planet."

*"Ah, sweet Transexual,
Land of night!
To sing and dance once more
to your dark refrains."*

"To take that step—to the right ..."

"With your hands on your hips!"

"But it's the pelvic THRUST!"

"That really drives you insane!"

"In our world ..."

"We'll do the Time Warp again!!!"

RRRRRRR

WHOOOSH!

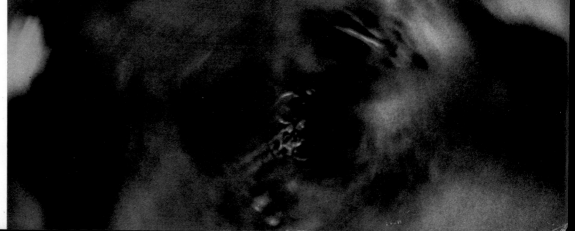

"And crawling on the planet's face,
Some insects called the human race.
Lost in time and lost in space—
And meaning."